Chemistry revision got you at boiling point?

Edexcel's 9-1 International GCSE Chemistry exams can get pretty heated, but this CGP book is a great way to stay cool and composed throughout your revision.

It's packed with thirty quick tests covering every IGCSE Chemistry topic*. Each one should only take ten minutes, so you won't need to block out hours of your life in one go. Just tackle them one at a time and you'll get there.

And finally, all the answers are included at the back of the book, so checking your work is a breeze! A cooling breeze, obviously.

* It's great for the Chemistry parts of the Edexcel International GCSE Science Double Award too.

CGP — still the best ☺

Our sole aim here at CGP is to produce the highest quality books — carefully written, immaculately presented and dangerously close to being funny.

Then we work our socks off to get them out to you — at the cheapest possible prices.

Published by CGP

Editors:
Alex Billings, Duncan Lindsay, Ethan Starmer-Jones

ISBN: 978 1 78908 086 5

With thanks to Karen Wells and Jamie Sinclair for the proofreading.

Clipart from Corel®
Printed by Elanders Ltd, Newcastle upon Tyne

Based on the classic CGP style created by Richard Parsons.

Contents

Paper 2

The questions in this book test both Chemistry Paper 1 and Chemistry Paper 2 material. Some material is needed for Paper 2 only — we've marked Paper 2 questions in Sections 1-6 with brackets like this one.

If you're doing a Science (Double Award) qualification you don't need to learn the Paper 2 material.

Section 1 — Particles and Mixtures

Test 1

There are **12 questions** in this test. Give yourself **10 minutes** to answer them all.

1. What name is given to the total number of protons and neutrons in an atom?

    A Isotopic abundance

    B Atomic number

    C Mass number

    [1]

2. True or False? "Chromatography can be used to separate out the different elements within a compound."

    A True

    B False

    [1]

3. Which of the following is used to separate mixtures in fractional distillation?

    A Differences in boiling point

    B Differences in melting point

    C Differences in solubility

    [1]

4. In which state of matter are the particles furthest apart?

    A Solid

    B Liquid

    C Gas

    [1]

5. In paper chromatography, the solvent...

    A ...forms a spot on the filter paper.

    B ...gradually moves up the filter paper.

    C ...is the mixture of substances being analysed.

    [1]

6. A liquid turns into a solid. What is this process called?

    A Freezing

    B Sublimation

    C Condensation

    [1]

7. Which of the following best describes how electrons are arranged in the atom?

    A Scattered in a ball of positive charge.

    B As a cloud within the nucleus.

    C In shells at fixed distances from the nucleus.

    [1]

8. The solubility of a substance is often measured in...

    A ...grams of solvent per 100 g of solute.

    B ...grams of solute per 100 g of solvent.

    C ...grams of solute per 100 g of solution.

    [1]

Paper 2

9. What are isotopes?

....

....

[1]

10. A student has a solution of red food colouring and water.
What will the student observe if she adds more water to the solution?
Explain your answer.

....

....

....

[2]

11. A student wants to use paper chromatography to determine the number of dyes used
in an ink. Describe how the student should set up this experiment.

....

....

....

....

....

[3]

12. A scientist is testing the melting point of water using a block of ice. They take samples
of the ice, and find that the samples they test reach their melting points over a range of
temperatures. Suggest why this is.

....

[1]

15

Test 2

There are **11 questions** in this test. Give yourself **10 minutes** to answer them all.

1. True or False? "Air is a chemically pure substance."

    A True

    B False

    [1]

2. Ammonia (NH_3) exists as...

    A ...molecules.

    B ...a pure element.

    C ...single atoms.

    [1]

3. An atom of phosphorus has atomic number 15 and mass number 31. Which of the following statements about this atom is true?

    A It has 15 protons and 16 electrons.

    B It has 15 electrons and 16 neutrons.

    C It has 15 neutrons and 16 protons.

    [1]

4. When a substance changes from a gas into a liquid...

    A ...the particles gain energy and move around faster.

    B ...the particles move further apart.

    C ...the particles lose energy and move closer together.

    [1]

5. Which change of state does not take place at the boiling point of a substance?

    A Freezing

    B Condensing

    C Boiling

    [1]

6. True or False? "Adding more solute to a saturated solution will increase the amount of solute dissolved in the solution."

    A True

    B False

    [1]

7. Which of the following processes can be used to obtain a sample of solid sugar from a water and sugar solution?

    A Filtration

    B Chromatography

    C Crystallisation

    [1]

8. True or False? "The A_r of an element takes into account the relative abundances of its isotopes."

    A True

    B False

    [1]

Section 1 — Particles and Mixtures

9. A student carried out paper chromatography on a pure substance. The solvent travelled 4.9 cm up the chromatography paper. The substance left a spot 3.2 cm up the paper. What is the R_f value of the substance? Give your answer to 2 significant figures.

$$R_f = \frac{\text{distance travelled by solute}}{\text{distance travelled by solvent}}$$

....

....

$R_f =$ ....

[2]

10. Explain how the pattern of spots produced in a paper chromatography experiment can be used to distinguish a pure substance from an impure substance.

....

....

[2]

11. A solubility curve for compound X is shown below.

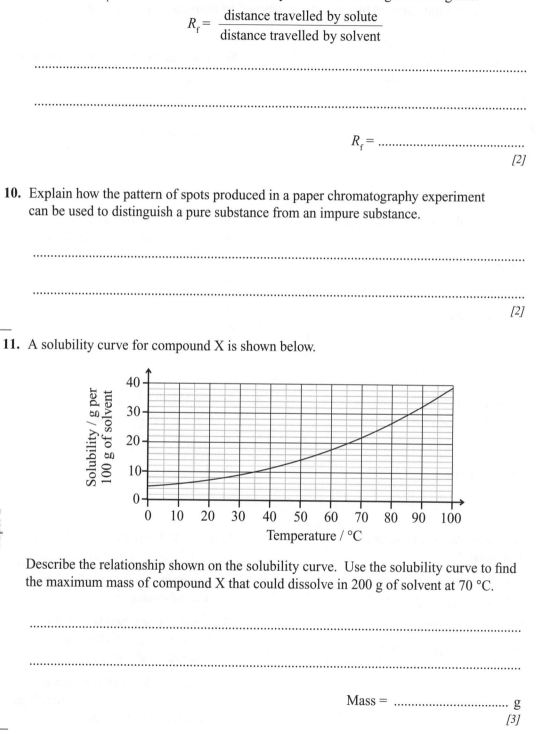

Describe the relationship shown on the solubility curve. Use the solubility curve to find the maximum mass of compound X that could dissolve in 200 g of solvent at 70 °C.

....

....

Mass = ... g

[3]

15

Test 3

⏱(10)

There are **12 questions** in this test. Give yourself **10 minutes** to answer them all.

1. Magnesium has 12 electrons.
    What is its electronic configuration?

    A　6.6

    B　8.4

    C　2.8.2

    [1]

2. What type of structure does graphite have?

    A　Giant covalent

    B　Simple molecular

    C　Ionic lattice

    [1]

3. What type of bond is formed when two
    hydrogen atoms form a molecule?

    A　An ionic bond

    B　A compound bond

    C　A covalent bond

    [1]

4. Beryllium is in Group 2 of the Periodic Table.
    What is the charge on a beryllium ion in an
    ionic compound?

    A　2+

    B　1+

    C　2–

    [1]

5. Giant covalent structures have high
    melting points because they contain...

    A　...strong covalent bonds.

    B　...strong intermolecular forces.

    [1]

6. True or False? "Simple molecular substances
    are generally good conductors of electricity."

    A　True

    B　False

    [1]

7. Which of the following properties is
    typical of metals?

    A　Their atoms have a full outer shell
    　　of electrons.

    B　They form acidic oxides.

    C　They can conduct electricity.

    [1]

8. In substances containing small molecules...

    A　...the intermolecular forces are much
    　　stronger than the covalent bonds within
    　　the molecules.

    B　...the covalent bonds within the
    　　molecules are much stronger than the
    　　intermolecular forces.

    C　...the covalent bonds within the
    　　molecules are the same strength as the
    　　intermolecular forces.

    [1]

Paper 2

9. In the Periodic Table, what do the electronic configurations of elements in the same group have in common?

    ....
    [1]

10. In which group of the Periodic Table would you find the noble gases?

    ....

    Why are the noble gases not very reactive?

    ....

    ....
    [2]

11. Sodium chloride has a giant ionic lattice structure.
    Describe the bonding in sodium chloride.

    ....

    ....

    ....

    ....
    [2]

12. Boron trioxide is a white solid with the formula B_2O_3.
    A scientist dissolves a sample of boron trioxide in a beaker of water. A solution forms.
    Suggest a value for the pH of the solution. Give a reason for your answer.

    ....

    ....

    ....
    [2]

    ┌──────┐
    │ 15 │
    └──────┘

Test 4

There are **11 questions** in this test. Give yourself **10 minutes** to answer them all.

1. True or False? "A group is a vertical column in the Periodic Table."

   A   True

   B   False

   [1]

2. What is the formula of a nitrate ion?

   A   NO

   B NO_3^-

   C N^{3-}

   [1]

3. Which of the following would you expect to have the lowest boiling point?

   A   A giant ionic structure

   B   A simple molecular structure

   C   A giant covalent structure

   [1]

4. True or False? "Ionic compounds conduct electricity when dissolved in water but not when molten."

   A   True

   B   False

   [1]

5. An ionic compound is made up of Na^+ ions and Br^- ions. What is its formula?

   A   NaBr

   B Na_2Br

   C $NaBr_2$

   [1]

6. A negative ion forms when an atom...

   A   ...gains electrons.

   B   ...loses electrons.

   C   ...forms a covalent bond.

   [1]

7. Which of the following is a compound that is made up of only non-metal atoms?

   A Na_2O

   B $CBrCl_3$

   C Ca_2SiO_4

   [1]

8. C_{60} fullerene is...

   A   ...a simple ionic substance that is a good conductor of electricity.

   B   ...a giant covalent substance that is a solid at room temperature.

   C   ...a simple molecular substance that contains delocalised electrons.

   [1]

Section 2 — The Periodic Table and Bonding

9. Describe the bonding in an O_2 molecule.

....

....

....
[2]

10. Explain why lithium, sodium and potassium all have similar chemical properties.

....

....

....
[2]

11. The diagram below shows part of the structure of a sample of potassium metal.

What do the labels **X** and **Y** represent on the diagram above?

X = ...   Y = ...

Using the diagram, explain how the structure and bonding of potassium affects its electrical conductivity and malleability.

....

....

....

....
[3]

15

Paper 2

Section 2 — The Periodic Table and Bonding

Test 5

There are **11 questions** in this test. Give yourself **10 minutes** to answer them all.

1. True or False? "One mole of oxygen contains more molecules than one mole of hydrogen."

   A   True

   B   False

   [1]

2. The molecular formula of butanoic acid is $C_4H_8O_2$. What is its empirical formula?

   A C_2H_4O

   B CH_2O

   C   CHO

   [1]

3. What is the relative formula mass (M_r) of KOH? Relative atomic masses (A_r): H = 1, O = 16, K = 39

   A   39

   B   28

   C   56

   [1]

4. During electrolysis, anions move towards the...

   A   ...positively charged electrode.

   B   ...negatively charged electrode.

   [1]

   Paper 2

5. In the following example, what physical state is the hydrochloric acid in?
   $Mg_{(s)} + 2HCl_{(aq)} \rightarrow MgCl_{2\,(aq)} + H_{2\,(g)}$

   A   Solid

   B   Gas

   C   Aqueous solution

   [1]

6. In the chemical reaction below, if 3 mol of chlorine molecules (Cl_2) react with excess potassium iodide (KI), how many moles of potassium chloride (KCl) are produced?

   $Cl_2 + 2KI \rightarrow I_2 + 2KCl$

   A   1.5 mol

   B   6 mol

   C   9 mol

   [1]

7. True or False? "The difference between a salt's hydrated mass and its anhydrous mass is equal to the mass of its water of crystallisation."

   A   True

   B   False

   [1]

8. Which of the following techniques would **not** be used to determine the formula of an anhydrous metal oxide?

   A   Hydration of the metal oxide

   B   Combustion of the metal

   C   Reduction of the metal oxide

   [1]

9. Balance the following chemical equation:

    $$........Li + ...H_2O \rightarrow ....LiOH + ...H_2$$

    [1]

10. 0.00025 kg of NaOH is dissolved in 0.5 dm³ of water.
    What is the concentration of the solution, in mol dm⁻³?

    Relative atomic masses (A_r): Na = 23, O = 16, H = 1

    ....

    ....

    ....

    ....

    ....

    .... mol dm⁻³
    [3]

11. A student heats a known mass of magnesium ribbon in a clean crucible of known mass.
    Describe how the student can use this to determine the empirical formula of
    magnesium oxide.

    ....

    ....

    ....

    ....

    ....

    ....

    ....
    [3]

    | 15 |

Paper 2

Test 6

🕐(10)

There are **11 questions** in this test. Give yourself **10 minutes** to answer them all.

1. What is the mass of one mole of $^{12}_{6}C$?

   A   18 g

   B   6 g

   C   12 g

   [1]

2. A formula that gives the smallest whole number ratio of atoms in a compound is...

   A   ...the empirical formula.

   B   ...the molecular formula.

   C   ...the relative formula.

   [1]

3. How can you calculate the number of moles of a substance, given its mass in grams?

   A   Mass ÷ relative formula mass

   B   Relative formula mass ÷ mass

   C   Relative formula mass × mass

   [1]

4. In the following chemical equation, what number should come before HCl to balance the equation?
   $$Zn + HCl \rightarrow ZnCl_2 + H_2$$

   A   1

   B   2

   C   3

   [1]

5. An aqueous solution of sodium chloride is electrolysed using inert electrodes. What are the products of the electrolysis?

   A   Sodium metal and oxygen

   B   Hydrogen gas and chlorine gas

   C   Sodium metal and chlorine gas

   [1]

6. A reaction has a theoretical yield of 45 g of product, but an actual yield of 36 g. What is the percentage yield of the reaction?

   A   20%

   B   125%

   C   80%

   [1]

7. The empirical formula of a compound is CH_2O. If there are 6 atoms of carbon in a single molecule of the compound, what is its molecular formula?

   A $C_6H_7O_6$

   B $C_6H_6O_{12}$

   C $C_6H_{12}O_6$

   [1]

8. The relative formula mass of a sulfate, ZSO_4, is 159.5. The relative atomic mass (A_r) of sulfur (S) = 32, and of oxygen (O) = 16. What is the relative atomic mass of element Z?

   A   63.5

   B   32.5

   C   15.5

   [1]

Paper 2

Section 3 — Equations, Calculations and Electrolysis

9. Molten lead bromide is made up of Pb^{2+} and Br^- ions.

It is electrolysed using inert electrodes.

Write the ionic half-equation for the reaction that occurs at the cathode.

....

[1]

10. 66 g of carbon are burnt completely in oxygen to produce CO_2.

The equation for the reaction is: $C + O_2 \rightarrow CO_2$.

Calculate the mass of CO_2 produced.

Relative atomic masses (A_r): C = 12, O = 16

....

....

....

....

....

.... g

[3]

11. In an experiment, 14.5 g of iron oxide powder is reduced to 10.5 g of pure metallic iron.
Use this data to find the empirical formula of the iron oxide.
Relative atomic mass (A_r): iron (Fe) = 56, oxygen (O) = 16

....

....

....

....

....

[3]

15

Section 4 — Inorganic Chemistry

Test 7

⏱ 10

There are **12 questions** in this test. Give yourself **10 minutes** to answer them all.

1. True or False? "The further down Group 7 you go, the more reactive the elements get."

   A   True

   B   False

[1]

2. At room temperature, chlorine (Cl_2) is...

   A   ...a yellow liquid.

   B   ...an orange gas.

   C   ...a green gas.

[1]

3. What does a pH of 7 indicate?

   A   An acidic solution

   B   An alkaline solution

   C   A neutral solution

[1]

4. True or False? "An insoluble base will react with an acid."

   A   True

   B   False

[1]

5. Which of the following metals is most easily oxidised?

   A   Silver

   B   Sodium

   C   Aluminium

[1]

6. Two metals, Q and R, are tested for their reactions with water. Metal Q reacted with cold water. Metal R reacted with steam, but not with cold water. Which is the more reactive metal?

   A   Metal Q

   B   Metal R

[1]

7. Which two things are needed for iron to rust?

   A   Carbon dioxide and hydrogen

   B   Carbon dioxide and water

   C   Oxygen and water

[1]

8. True or False? "Iron can be extracted by reduction using carbon, because iron is less reactive than carbon."

   A   True

   B   False

[1]

Paper 2

9. How can limewater be used to test for carbon dioxide?

....

....

[1]

10. A student adds a few drops of methyl orange to some dilute hydrochloric acid.
She then slowly adds calcium oxide powder to the solution, until no more will react.
Describe the colour change that the student will observe in the solution.

....

[1]

11. Name **two** metal chlorides that are insoluble in water.

1: ....

2: ....

[2]

12. A student added pieces of magnesium and iron to two beakers of hydrochloric acid.
She noticed that magnesium reacted faster than iron. Describe what the student saw
that led her to this conclusion, and explain why magnesium reacts faster than iron.

....

....

....

....

....

[3]

15

Test 8

There are **11 questions** in this test. Give yourself **10 minutes** to answer them all.

1. What is an alkali?

    A A soluble base

    B A soluble acid

    C An insoluble base

    [1]

2. Which of the following metals reacts most vigorously with water?

    A Lithium

    B Sodium

    C Potassium

    [1]

3. True or False? "Carbon dioxide is the most abundant gas in the atmosphere today."

    A True

    B False

    [1]

4. Oxidation is...

    A ...gain of electrons.

    B ...loss of electrons.

    [1]

5. What is the chemical test for hydrogen?

    A It burns with a green flame.

    B It turns damp litmus paper white.

    C It burns with a squeaky pop.

    [1]

6. True or False? "Anhydrous copper(II) sulfate turns blue in the presence of water."

    A True

    B False

    [1]

7. A solution of potassium hydroxide reacts with nitric acid to produce...

    A ...carbon dioxide and water.

    B ...a metal oxide and water.

    C ...a salt and water.

    [1]

8. Why might iron be galvanised with zinc?

    A Zinc is less reactive than iron so it gives a protective coating around the iron.

    B Zinc is more reactive than iron so water and oxygen will react with zinc instead of with the iron.

    C To give the iron a lower density.

    [1]

9. A student is carrying out a flame test to identify the metal ion that is present in a sample.
She dips a platinum wire loop in some dilute hydrochloric acid to clean it.
Describe what the student should do next in order to complete the flame test.

....

....

....

....

[2]

10. Describe how increasing the amount of carbon dioxide gas in the Earth's atmosphere
causes the warming of the surface of the Earth.

....

....

....

....

....

....

[3]

11. Why do Group 1 elements become more reactive as you go down the group?

....

....

....

....

[2]

15

Section 4 — Inorganic Chemistry

Paper 2

Test 9

There are **11 questions** in this test. Give yourself **10 minutes** to answer them all.

1. In a flame test, which of these metal ions burns to give a blue-green flame?

   A Cu^{2+}

   B Ca^{2+}

   C K^+

   [1]

2. True or False? "Hydroxide ions make solutions acidic."

   A True

   B False

   [1]

3. Which Group 7 element is a dark grey crystalline solid at room temperature?

   A Fluorine

   B Bromine

   C Iodine

   [1]

4. Which of the following elements burns in oxygen to produce a solid?

   A Hydrogen

   B Magnesium

   C Sulfur

   [1]

5. True or False? "A solution with a pH of 1 is very acidic."

   A True

   B False

   [1]

6. What is the approximate percentage of nitrogen in the Earth's atmosphere?

   A 78%

   B 21%

   C 1%

   [1]

7. Sodium is higher in the reactivity series than iron. This means that...

   A ...iron will displace sodium from sodium oxide.

   B ...sodium will displace iron from iron oxide.

   C ...neither metal will be able to displace the other metal from its oxide.

   [1]

8. Which of the following metals has carbon added to it to make the alloy steel?

   Paper 2

   A Copper

   B Aluminium

   C Iron

   [1]

Section 4 — Inorganic Chemistry

9. Copper sulfate can be produced using the following reaction:

$$CuO_{(s)} + H_2SO_{4(aq)} \rightarrow CuSO_{4(aq)} + H_2O_{(l)}$$

The reaction produces a solution of copper sulfate dissolved in water.
Describe how pure, dry crystals of copper sulfate can be produced from this solution.

....

....

....

....

....

[3]

10. A student adds some dilute hydrochloric acid to a solution of sulfate ions.
She then adds some barium chloride solution.
What will the student observe when she adds the barium chloride solution?

....

....

[1]

11. Explain the trend in the reactivity of the halogens down the group.

....

....

....

....

....

[3]

15

Paper 2

Test 10

There are **11 questions** in this test. Give yourself **10 minutes** to answer them all.

1. What colour is the flame produced when a calcium compound is burnt in a flame test?

   A Green

   B Orange-red

   C Yellow

   [1]

2. Which gas is produced when a metal carbonate reacts with dilute acid?

   A Carbon dioxide

   B Hydrogen

   C Oxygen

   [1]

3. True or False? "All nitrates are soluble in water."

   A True

   B False

   [1]

4. Sacrificial protection is a process where a metal is coated with...

   A ...a less reactive metal.

   B ...a more reactive metal.

   C ...a layer of paint.

   [1]

5. The products of the thermal decomposition of copper carbonate are...

   A ...copper oxide and water.

   B ...copper hydroxide and carbon dioxide.

   C ...copper oxide and carbon dioxide.

   [1]

6. What happens to a reducing agent during a redox reaction?

   A It is oxidised.

   B It is reduced.

   C It is chemically unchanged.

   [1]

7. A scientist has a solution with a pH of 10. What colour would the solution turn if universal indicator was added?

   A Red

   B Green

   C Purple

   [1]

8. Which of the following mixtures can be described as an alloy?

   A carbon and sulfur

   B iron and carbon

   C water and zinc

   [1]

   Paper 2

Section 4 — Inorganic Chemistry

9. Potassium reacts with water in a vigorous reaction. Copper does not react with water. What do these results tell you about the relative positions of potassium and copper in the reactivity series? Explain your answer.

....

....

....

....

[2]

10. Suggest the name of **one** metal which can be found as an uncombined element in the Earth's crust. Explain your answer.

....

....

[2]

11. A student is carrying out a reaction to determine the percentage of oxygen in the air. She heats a sample of phosphorus in the apparatus shown below.

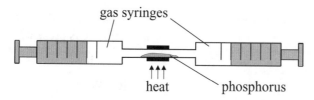

gas syringes

heat   phosphorus

The apparatus contained 59.0 cm³ of gas before the phosphorus was heated.
At the end of the reaction, the apparatus contained 47.0 cm³ of gas.
Use this information to calculate the percentage of oxygen in the air.
Give your answer to 3 significant figures.

....

....

....

.... %

[3]

15

Test 11

There are **11 questions** in this test. Give yourself **10 minutes** to answer them all.

1. Reduction is...

   A ...removal of oxygen.

   B ...gain of oxygen.

[1]

2. True or False? "Under standard conditions, pure water will always boil at 100 °C."

   A True

   B False

[1]

3. Which of the following compounds is insoluble in water?

   A Potassium sulfate

   B Sodium sulfate

   C Barium sulfate

[1]

4. Chlorine has a boiling point of −34 °C. Bromine has a boiling point of 59 °C. What is the boiling point of iodine?

   A 185 °C

   B 25 °C

   C −93 °C

[1]

5. What colour does phenolphthalein turn in alkaline solutions?

   A Blue

   B Colourless

   C Pink

[1]

6. What colour does damp litmus paper turn if chlorine is present?

   A Blue

   B White

   C Green

[1]

7. Which halogen is a red-brown liquid at room temperature?

   A Chlorine

   B Bromine

   C Iodine

[1]

8. Why is aluminium often used to make parts of aeroplanes?

   A Aluminium has a low density.

   B Aluminium is a good conductor of heat.

   C Aluminium has a low melting point.

[1]

Paper 2

9. A student is testing a solution, X, for the presence of ammonium ions, NH_4^+.
    The student adds sodium hydroxide to solution X and collects the gas that is produced.
    How could the student test the gas to determine if solution X contains NH_4^+?

    ....

    ....

    ....

    ....

    [2]

10. The equation below shows a neutralisation reaction.
    $$H_2SO_4 + Na_2CO_3 \rightarrow Na_2SO_4 + H_2O + CO_2$$
    Identify the proton acceptor and the proton donor in this reaction.

    Proton acceptor: ....

    Proton donor: ....

    [2]

11. Aqueous lead(II) nitrate ($Pb(NO_3)_2$) reacts with aqueous magnesium sulfate ($MgSO_4$).
    The reaction forms one insoluble salt and one soluble salt.
    Write a symbol equation for this reaction. Include state symbols in your answer.

    ....

    The insoluble salt can be separated from the reaction mixture using filtration.
    Filtration involves rinsing the insoluble salt to remove any soluble substances.
    Explain why deionised water should be used throughout the filtration process,
    in order to produce a pure sample of the insoluble salt.

    ....

    ....

    ....

    [3]

    15

Paper 2

Test 12

There are **11 questions** in this test. Give yourself **10 minutes** to answer them all.

1. True or False? "Group 1 metals all react with water in a similar way."

   A   True

   B   False

   [1]

2. What is produced when hydrogen undergoes a combustion reaction in air?

   A   Carbon dioxide and water

   B   Water only

   C   Carbon dioxide only

   [1]

3. Calcium hydroxide is...

   A   ...insoluble in water.

   B   ...slightly soluble in water.

   C   ...very soluble in water.

   [1]

4. Sodium hydroxide solution is added to a solution containing Fe^{2+} ions.
   What is the colour of the precipitate formed?

   A   Sludgy green

   B   Blue

   C   Reddish brown

   [1]

5. A student places a glowing splint into a test tube containing a gas. The splint relights. Which gas is present in the test tube?

   A   Hydrogen

   B   Carbon dioxide

   C   Oxygen

   [1]

6. Which of the following pH values could a concentrated strong alkali have?

   A   1.5

   B   13.8

   C   8.2

   [1]

7. Which of the following statements about carbon dioxide is **not** true?

   A   Carbon dioxide is a greenhouse gas.

   B   The percentage of carbon dioxide in the Earth's atmosphere is around 0.04%.

   C   Carbon dioxide is produced when sodium sulfate reacts with nitric acid.

   [1]

8. In an acid-alkali titration...

   A   ...a pipette should be used to add the acid to the alkali.

   B   ...an indicator can be used to determine when the reaction is complete.

   C   ...the concentration of acid used must be equal to the concentration of the alkali.

   [1]

Paper 2

Section 4 — Inorganic Chemistry

9. Describe how barrier methods are used to prevent iron from rusting.

....

....

....

[2]

10. The equation below shows the neutralisation reaction between hydrochloric acid and sodium hydroxide.

$$HCl + NaOH \rightarrow NaCl + H_2O$$

Write a symbol equation to show how the hydrogen ions and hydroxide ions react with each other during this neutralisation reaction.

....

What will the pH of a pure NaCl solution be?

....

[2]

11. Titanium is more reactive than zinc but is less reactive than magnesium. The final step in the extraction of titanium from its ore is shown below.

$$TiCl_4 + 4Na \rightarrow Ti + 4NaCl$$

Suggest why sodium is a suitable metal to use in this reaction.
Give **one** example of a metal that could **not** be used to extract titanium in this way.

....

....

....

....

....

[3]

Paper 2

15

Section 5 — Physical Chemistry

Test 13

⏱ 10

There are **11 questions** in this test. Give yourself **10 minutes** to answer them all.

1. How does a catalyst increase a reaction's rate?

   A It shifts the position of equilibrium.

   B It increases the energy of the reactants.

   C It decreases the activation energy needed.

   [1]

2. True or False? "In a reaction between gases, increasing the pressure of the reaction mixture will increase the reaction rate."

   A True

   B False

   [1]

3. Increasing the temperature of a reaction mixture increases the rate of the reaction because...

   A ...there are fewer collisions.

   B ...the energy of the collisions is greater.

   C ...there are more particles of reactant in the same volume.

   [1]

4. Which of the following can be used to measure the heat energy change when a chemical reaction takes place?

   A Change in colour

   B Change in specific heat capacity

   C Change in temperature

   [1]

5. What is the activation energy of a reaction?

   A The total energy of the reactants.

   B The minimum amount of energy needed by the particles to react.

   C The maximum amount of energy needed by the particles to react.

   [1]

6. What does the symbol '$\rightleftharpoons$' tell you about the reaction shown below?
   $$2SO_2 + O_2 \rightleftharpoons 2SO_3$$

   A The reaction is exothermic.

   B The reaction is an oxidation reaction.

   C The reaction is reversible.

   [1]

7. For a reversible reaction that occurs in a sealed reaction vessel, when is dynamic equilibrium reached?

   A When all the reactants are used up.

   B When the amounts of products and reactants are equal.

   C When the rates of the forward and reverse reactions are equal.

   [1]

8. If the surroundings increase in temperature during a reaction...

   A ...the reaction is endothermic.

   B ...the reaction is exothermic.

   C ...the molar enthalpy change of the reaction is positive.

   [1]

Paper 2

Section 5 — Physical Chemistry

9. Explain, in terms of particle collisions, why increasing the concentration of reacting solutions increases the rate of a reaction.

....

....

....

[2]

10. The combustion of methanol is an exothermic reaction.
In an experiment, 1.64 g of methanol combusts to heat 150 g of water by 53 °C.
Use this experimental data to calculate the molar enthalpy change of this reaction.
Specific heat capacity (c) of water = 4.2 J/g/°C.
Relative formula mass (M_r) of methanol = 32.

....

....

....

....

....

.... kJ/mol
[3]

11. The equation below shows a reversible reaction, where A, B, C and D are different gases.

$$2A + B \rightleftharpoons C + D$$

What would happen to the position of equilibrium if the pressure were increased?
Explain your answer.

....

....

....

[2]

15

Section 5 — Physical Chemistry

Paper 2

Test 14

There are **11 questions** in this test. Give yourself **10 minutes** to answer them all.

1. True or False? "A catalyst will always be chemically changed when it is used to increase the rate of a reaction."

   A True

   B False

   [1]

2. In a reaction between marble and hydrochloric acid, using small marble chips instead of a large piece of marble will produce...

   A ...no difference in the rate of reaction.

   B ...a slower rate of reaction.

   C ...a faster rate of reaction.

   [1]

3. 150 g of water is heated from 20 °C to 45 °C. The specific heat capacity of water is 4.2 J/g/°C. How much heat energy is transferred to the water?

   A 15.75 J

   B 15 750 J

   C 40 950 J

   [1]

4. Which of the following will increase the rate of reaction between two aqueous solutions?

   A Making the solutions less concentrated.

   B Using a bigger reaction vessel.

   C Increasing the average energy of the collisions.

   [1]

5. True or False? "The dehydration of hydrated copper(II) sulfate is a reversible reaction."

   A True

   B False

   [1]

6. Breaking a chemical bond...

   A ...is an endothermic process.

   B ...is an exothermic process.

   [1]

Paper 2

7. Which of the following would **not** be suitable for measuring the rate of the decomposition reaction of hydrogen peroxide?

   A Measuring the volume of gas produced over time.

   B Measuring the mass lost from the reaction vessel over time.

   C Measuring how the colour of the solution changes over time.

   [1]

8. Which of the following pieces of equipment would you **not** need when carrying out a calorimetry experiment to measure the enthalpy change of a displacement reaction?

   A A Bunsen burner

   B A thermometer

   C A well-insulated container

   [1]

Section 5 — Physical Chemistry

9. The diagram shows the results of the same reaction carried out in two different experiments.

Suggest **one** way in which the conditions in experiment 2 could have been different to those in experiment 1. Explain your answer.

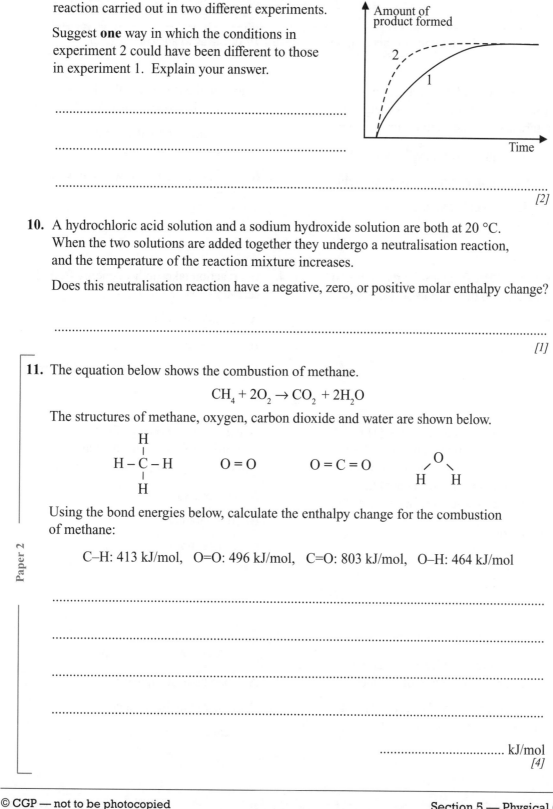

....

....

....

[2]

10. A hydrochloric acid solution and a sodium hydroxide solution are both at 20 °C. When the two solutions are added together they undergo a neutralisation reaction, and the temperature of the reaction mixture increases.

Does this neutralisation reaction have a negative, zero, or positive molar enthalpy change?

....

[1]

11. The equation below shows the combustion of methane.

$$CH_4 + 2O_2 \rightarrow CO_2 + 2H_2O$$

The structures of methane, oxygen, carbon dioxide and water are shown below.

$$H-\overset{\overset{\displaystyle H}{|}}{\underset{\underset{\displaystyle H}{|}}{C}}-H \qquad O=O \qquad O=C=O \qquad \overset{O}{\underset{H \quad H}{\diagup \; \diagdown}}$$

Using the bond energies below, calculate the enthalpy change for the combustion of methane:

C–H: 413 kJ/mol,   O=O: 496 kJ/mol,   C=O: 803 kJ/mol,   O–H: 464 kJ/mol

....

....

....

....

.... kJ/mol

[4]

15

Paper 2

Section 5 — Physical Chemistry

Test 15

⏱ 10

There are **11 questions** in this test. Give yourself **10 minutes** to answer them all.

1. The forward reaction of an equilibrium is exothermic. What effect will decreasing the temperature have on the equilibrium position?

   A   The equilibrium position will move left.

   B   The equilibrium position will move right.

   C   It will have no effect on the equilibrium position.
   [1]

2. Changing the catalyst in the decomposition reaction of hydrogen peroxide (H_2O_2) will...

   A   ...change the total volume of oxygen (O_2) produced.

   B   ...change the rate at which oxygen is produced.
   [1]

3. True or False? "Breaking a solid reactant into smaller pieces will decrease its surface area."

   A   True

   B   False
   [1]

4. If a reaction takes in heat energy from the surroundings, the reaction is...

   A   ...endothermic.

   B   ...exothermic.

   C   ...neither exothermic nor endothermic.
   [1]

5. A fuel has a relative molecular mass (M_r) of 46.0. 92.0 g of the fuel transfers 2720 kJ of heat to the surroundings when it is burned. What is the molar enthalpy change of the reaction that occurs when the fuel is burned?

   A   29.6 kJ/mol

   B   59.1 kJ/mol

   C   1360 kJ/mol
   [1]

6. Which of the following affects the proportion of collisions that have enough energy for particles to react?

   A   Gas pressure

   B   Temperature

   C   Concentration
   [1]

7. If a reaction is at dynamic equilibrium...

   A   ...the concentration of reactants is the same as the concentration of products.

   B   ...the concentration of the reactants and products remains constant over time.
   [1]

8. In the equation $Q = m \times c \times \Delta T$, what does the variable c represent?

   A   specific heat capacity

   B   molar enthalpy change

   C   heat energy change
   [1]

Section 5 — Physical Chemistry

9. Marble chips react with hydrochloric acid to form calcium chloride, carbon dioxide and water. Describe an experiment that could be used to investigate the effect of changing the concentration of hydrochloric acid on the rate of the reaction.

....

....

....

....

....

....

[3]

10. Does the reaction profile on the right show an exothermic or an endothermic reaction? Explain your answer.

Energy

Progress of Reaction

....

....

....

[2]

11. Ammonium chloride is a white solid. A student heats a sample of ammonium chloride in a sealed reaction vessel until it breaks down to form hydrogen chloride gas and ammonia gas. Explain how the student could show that this reaction is reversible.

....

....

....

[2]

15

Test 16

There are **11 questions** in this test. Give yourself **10 minutes** to answer them all.

1. What is the structural formula of ethane?

   A CH_2CH_2

   B CH_3CH_3

   C $CH_3CH_2CH_2$

   [1]

2. Carbon monoxide is...

   A   ...a toxic gas.

   B   ...a hydrocarbon.

   C   ...a cause of acid rain.

   [1]

3. Which of the following is a use of the fuel oil fraction of crude oil?

   A   Fuel for cars

   B   Fuel for aircraft

   C   Fuel for large ships

   [1]

4. Which of the following does **not** vary for different members of the same homologous series of compounds?

   A   Molecular formula

   B   Functional group

   C   Length of molecule

   [1]

5. Bromine water will turn from orange to colourless when added to a sample of...

   A   ...methane.

   B   ...ethane.

   C   ...ethene.

   [1]

6. How many C–C single bonds are there in one molecule of propene?

   A   0

   B   1

   C   2

   [1]

7. What is the main problem with using fuels that contain sulfur impurities?

   A   The fuel produces more soot when it burns.

   B   The fuel produces emissions which can cause acid rain.

   C   The fuel is more expensive.

   [1]

8. Ethanediol can react with ethanedioic acid to form poly(ethyl ethanoate). What sort of reaction is this?

   A   Condensation polymerisation

   B   Addition polymerisation

   C   Combustion

   [1]

Paper 2

---

9. Why are alkenes described as unsaturated?

....

....

[1]

10. Gaseous crude oil is piped into the bottom of a fractionating column.
Explain how it is then separated into different fractions.

....

....

....

....

....

[3]

11. A section of poly(propene) is shown on the right.

$$\left(\begin{array}{cc} H & H \\ | & | \\ -C & -C- \\ | & | \\ H & CH_3 \end{array}\right)_n$$

What type of polymer is poly(propene)?

....

Give **two** problems associated with the disposal of polymers such as poly(propene).

....

....

....

....

[3]

15

Test 17

⏱ 10

There are **11 questions** in this test. Give yourself **10 minutes** to answer them all.

1. True or False? "The demand for short-chain hydrocarbons is higher than the demand for long-chain hydrocarbons."

   A   True

   B   False

   [1]

2. Nitrogen oxides can form when...

   A   ...fuels burn at low temperatures.

   B   ...fuels burn at high temperatures.

   [1]

3. Which technique is used to separate the components of crude oil?

   A   Cracking

   B   Filtration

   C   Fractional distillation

   [1]

4. How many carbon atoms are there in one molecule of but-2-ene?

   A   2

   B   4

   C   6

   [1]

5. Carbon and carbon monoxide can be produced in combustion reactions where...

   A   ...there is not enough nitrogen.

   B   ...there is not enough fuel.

   C   ...there is not enough oxygen.

   [1]

6. What reagent and conditions are used to convert methane into bromomethane?

   A Br_2 and ultraviolet light

   B Br_2 and heat

   C O_2 and ultraviolet light

   [1]

7. Which of these is not an alcohol?

   A   Methanol

   B   Butane

   C   Propanol

   [1]

Paper 2

8. True or False? "Vinegar contains ethanoic acid."

   A   True

   B   False

   [1]

Paper 2

9. Name **two** substances produced during hydrocarbon fuel combustion that can lead to the formation of acid rain.

1. ....

2. ....

[2]

10. Hydrocarbon E has the structural formula $CH_3CH_2CH_2CH_2CH_3$.
Draw the displayed formula of hydrocarbon E.

Name hydrocarbon E.

....

[2]

11. Describe how catalytic cracking is used to convert long-chain alkanes into more useful products. Include any reaction conditions in your answer.

....

....

....

....

....

[3]

15

Test 18

🕙 10

There are **11 questions** in this test. Give yourself **10 minutes** to answer them all.

1. What is the functional group of an alkene?

   A C=C

   B C–C

   C C=H

   [1]

2. True or False? "All hydrocarbons contain carbon and hydrogen, but some hydrocarbons also contain oxygen."

   A True

   B False

   [1]

3. Which of the following crude oil fractions is used to surface roads?

   A Bitumen

   B Diesel

   C Kerosene

   [1]

4. Which of these is **not** produced when a hydrocarbon fuel undergoes complete combustion?

   A Carbon dioxide

   B Water

   C Carbon monoxide

   [1]

5. The molecular formula of a compound is $C_6H_{12}O_6$. What is its empirical formula?

   A C_2H_4O

   B CH_2O

   C CHO

   [1]

6. A fuel is a substance that...

   A ...reacts with oxygen to produce a hydrocarbon.

   B ...can be cracked to produce smaller fuel molecules.

   C ...releases heat energy when it is burned.

   [1]

7. True or False? "Cracking is used to turn long-chain hydrocarbons into short-chain hydrocarbons."

   A True

   B False

   [1]

8. Ethanol can be oxidised to produce...

   A ...an ester.

   B ...ethanoic acid.

   C ...ethene.

   [1]

Paper 2

Section 6 — Organic Chemistry

© CGP — not to be photocopied

9. Name the product formed in the reaction shown on the right.
Explain why ethene can undergo this reaction.

$$n \begin{pmatrix} \overset{\displaystyle H}{\underset{\displaystyle H}{|}} \\ C = C \\ \overset{\displaystyle H}{\underset{\displaystyle H}{|}} \end{pmatrix} \longrightarrow \begin{pmatrix} \overset{\displaystyle H}{\underset{\displaystyle H}{|}} \\ C - C \\ \overset{\displaystyle H}{\underset{\displaystyle H}{|}} \end{pmatrix}_n$$

ethene

....

....

[2]

10. Bromine can react with propene. The product of the reaction is a dibromoalkane.
Write a balanced symbol equation for this reaction.

....

[1]

11. Ethanol and ethanoic acid can react to form an ester. When carried out in the lab,
a few drops of sulfuric acid are added to the reaction mixture.
State the purpose of the sulfuric acid in this reaction.

....

....

Name the products of the reaction.

....

Draw the displayed formula of the ester produced in the experiment.

[4]

15

Section 6 — Organic Chemistry

Paper 2

Test 19

⏱ 10

There are **11 questions** in this test. Give yourself **10 minutes** to answer them all.

1. Why is cracking of hydrocarbons carried out?

A To purify the fractions of crude oil.

B To generate electricity.

C To convert long alkane molecules into smaller, more useful molecules.

[1]

2. A hydrocarbon reacts with oxygen to produce carbon dioxide and water. This is an example of...

A ...combustion.

B ...an addition reaction.

C ...a substitution reaction.

[1]

3. True or False? "Alkanes are unsaturated molecules."

A True

B False

[1]

4. Which of the following fractions of crude oil is the most viscous?

A Gasoline

B Diesel

C Bitumen

[1]

5. Why is carbon monoxide a dangerous pollutant?

A It stops the blood carrying oxygen around the body.

B It causes acid rain.

C It builds up in the lungs and blocks the airways.

[1]

6. Which of the following is a reason why addition polymers are difficult to dispose of?

A They break down in the environment to form monomers.

B They can not be burned.

C They are inert.

[1]

7. When a polyester forms...

A ...double bonds in the monomers open up.

B ...carbon dioxide is given off.

C ...water molecules are also formed.

[1]

Paper 2

8. What is the functional group of an alcohol?

A –OH

B –C=O

C –COOH

[1]

Paper 2

Section 6 — Organic Chemistry

9. PVDF is an addition polymer which is used to insulate electrical wires. The formula of PVDF is shown on the right.

Draw the displayed formula of the monomer used to make PVDF.

[1]

10. A student shakes a solution of bromine water with a sample of an alkene. What will the student observe? Describe the reaction that occurs.

....

....

....

....

[3]

11. An isomer of an alkene containing four carbon atoms is shown on the right.

Give the full IUPAC name of this isomer.

....

Draw the displayed formulas of **two** more isomers of this alkene.

[3]

15

Test 20

There are **11 questions** in this test. Give yourself **10 minutes** to answer them all.

1. True or False? "Oxides of nitrogen are harmful pollutants."

   A   True

   B   False

   [1]

2. What is the general formula of alkanes?

   A C_nH_{2n}

   B C_nH_{2n+2}

   C $C_{2n}H_n$

   [1]

3. A functional group is...

   A   ...a group of atoms that determines how a compound reacts.

   B   ...a group of compounds that all have the same general formula.

   C   ...the most reactive part of a molecule.

   [1]

4. Which of the following statements about acid rain is false?

   A   It forms when nitrogen oxides mix with clouds.

   B   Burning fuels that contain sulfur impurities can contribute to acid rain.

   C   It releases soot into the atmosphere.

   [1]

5. Why can the hydrocarbons in crude oil be separated by fractional distillation?

   A   They have different boiling points.

   B   They have different melting points.

   C   They have different viscosities.

   [1]

6. Which of the following are produced by cracking?

   A   Alkanes and water vapour

   B   Alkanes and alkenes

   C   Only alkenes

   [1]

7. What is produced when an aqueous solution of glucose is fermented using yeast?

   A   Aqueous ethene and carbon dioxide

   B   Nitrogen and aqueous ethanol

   C   Carbon dioxide and aqueous ethanol

   [1]

Paper 2

8. True or False? "Condensation polymerisation involves monomers with a single functional group."

   A   True

   B   False

   [1]

Paper 2

Section 6 — Organic Chemistry

© CGP — not to be photocopied

9. In the presence of ultraviolet light, iodine can react with butane.
    Write a balanced symbol equation for this reaction.

    ....

    How many isomers of the organic product could be produced in the reaction?

    ....

    [2]

10. Give the two possible products of incomplete combustion of a hydrocarbon,
    other than carbon dioxide and water.

    1. ....

    2. ....

    [2]

11. What process is used to turn the long-chain hydrocarbons found in bitumen into the
    hydrocarbons found in kerosene? Explain why this process is necessary, in terms of the
    supply and demand of different fractions.

    ....

    ....

    ....

    ....

    ....

    ....

    [3]

    15

Test 21

This test covers **Paper 2** material **only**.
There are **11 questions** in this test. Give yourself **10 minutes** to answer them all.

1. True or False? "Ethanol is oxidised when it is burned in air."

   A True

   B False

   [1]

2. What is the structural formula of methanol?

   A CH_4

   B CH_3OH

   C CH_3CH_2OH

   [1]

3. Which small molecule is produced when a condensation polymer is formed?

   A Methane

   B Water

   C Carbon dioxide

   [1]

4. Which of the following statements about esters is **not** true?

   A Esters often have distinctive smells.

   B Esters contain oxygen atoms.

   C Esters always contain C=C bonds.

   [1]

5. Butyl propanoate is produced from...

   A ...butanol and propanoic acid.

   B ...propanol and butanoic acid.

   C ...butanol and water.

   [1]

6. What is the name given to biodegradable polyesters?

   A Condensation polyesters

   B Biopolyesters

   C Addition polyesters

   [1]

7. Which of the following carboxylic acids has the structural formula CH_3CH_2COOH?

   A Ethanoic acid

   B Butanoic acid

   C Propanoic acid

   [1]

8. What is the optimum temperature for the fermentation of glucose using yeast?

   A 600 °C

   B 300 °C

   C 30 °C

   [1]

Section 6 — Organic Chemistry

9. In industry, ethanol can be manufactured from ethene in the presence of a catalyst.
   Give the catalyst and the reaction conditions for this process.

   ....

   ....

   ....

   [3]

10. The repeat unit of a polyester, G, is shown below.

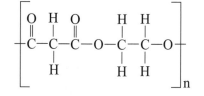

   Draw the displayed formulas of the two monomers that can undergo
   condensation polymerisation to form polyester G.

   [2]

11. A student reacts a small amount of sodium metal with a solution of methanoic acid.
    Write a balanced symbol equation for this reaction.

    ....

    Draw the displayed formula of the salt formed in the reaction.

    [2]

15

Test 22

There are **11 questions** in this test. Give yourself **10 minutes** to answer them all.

1. True or False? "Isotopes of the same element all have the same mass number."

   A   True

   B   False

   [1]

2. True or False? "Oxygen will relight a glowing splint."

   A   True

   B   False

   [1]

3. Which of the following statements about catalysts is true?

   A   They increase the activation energy required in order for particles to react.

   B   They increase the rate of a reaction.

   C   They are chemically altered in a reaction.

   [1]

4. Iron has an atomic number of 26. How many electrons does an Fe^{3+} ion have?

   A   23

   B   26

   C   29

   [1]

5. When a metal reacts completely to form a metal oxide, the mass of the metal oxide formed will be...

   A   ...greater than the mass of the metal used.

   B   ...less than the mass of the metal used.

   C   ...the same as the mass of the metal used.

   [1]

6. Which of the following statements about addition polymers is true?

   A   They always contain carbon-carbon double bonds.

   B   They biodegrade very quickly.

   C   They're made up of lots of small repeating units.

   [1]

7. In which group of the periodic table would you find the halogens?

   A   Group 1

   B   Group 7

   C   Group 6

   [1]

8. Which of the following reactions will produce a precipitate?

   A   Magnesium and nitric acid

   B   Sodium carbonate and hydrochloric acid

   C   Calcium and sulfuric acid

   [1]

9. Copper sulfate is a soluble salt produced in the reaction between copper oxide and sulfuric acid. Give **one** reason why excess copper oxide is added to the sulfuric acid during the production of copper sulfate.

....

....

[1]

10. A student has a sample of a hydrocarbon, X. No reaction occurs when she adds a few drops of bromine water to hydrocarbon X. When the student shines UV light on the resulting solution, the solution changes colour from orange to colourless.
Which homologous series does hydrocarbon X belong to?

....

Describe the reaction that occurs when the solution is exposed to UV light.
What type of reaction is this?

....

....

....

[3]

11. A student carried out an experiment to find the energy change of a neutralisation reaction. She added 25 g of each reactant solution to a polystyrene cup. The temperature of the reaction mixture increased by 18.5 °C. Both reactant solutions were at the same temperature before the reaction occurred.

Calculate the heat energy transferred during the reaction in kJ.
The specific heat capacity of the reaction mixture, $c = 4.2$ J/g/ °C.

....

....

....

Heat energy transferred = ... kJ

[3]

15

Test 23

⏱ 10

There are **11 questions** in this test. Give yourself **10 minutes** to answer them all.

1. Which of the following statements about chlorine is true?

    A   Chlorine is red-brown liquid at room temperature.

    B   The atomic number of chlorine is 9.

    C   Chlorine is more reactive than iodine.

    [1]

2. You can test for halide ions by adding dilute nitric acid to a solution followed by...

    A   ...limewater.

    B   ...silver nitrate solution.

    C   ...sodium hydroxide solution.

    [1]

3. Which type of chemical bonding involves a 'bonding pair' of electrons?

    A   Covalent bonding

    B   Metallic bonding

    C   Ionic bonding

    [1]

4. Which of the following cations produces a lilac flame in a flame test?

    A Li^+

    B Ca^{2+}

    C K^+

    [1]

5. What colour is phenolphthalein in acidic solutions?

    A   Pink

    B   Colourless

    C   Yellow

    [1]

6. Which of the following fractions of crude oil would you expect to be the palest in colour?

    A   Kerosene

    B   Bitumen

    C   Fuel Oil

    [1]

7. In paper chromatography, what is an R_f value?

    A   The distance travelled by the solvent, measured from the baseline.

    B   The amount of solute that has travelled above the baseline.

    C   The ratio between the distance travelled by the solute and the solvent.

    [1]

8. In a reaction between hydrochloric acid and marble chips...

    A   ...the rate of reaction depends on the size of the container.

    B   ...increasing the concentration of acid will increase the rate of reaction.

    C   ...the mass of the marble chips increases over time.

    [1]

Mixed Tests for Paper 1

9. The displayed formula of an organic compound is shown on the right.

H—C—C—C—C—H (with H atoms above and below each carbon)

Give the name and the empirical formula of the compound.

Name: ....

Empirical formula: ....

[2]

10. A student has a mixture of magnesium sulfate and copper filings.
Magnesium sulfate is a solid that is soluble in water. Outline a method that
the student could use to obtain a pure sample of the magnesium sulfate.

....

....

....

....

....

[3]

11. The graph on the right shows how the volume
of gas produced in three hydrogen peroxide
decomposition reactions changed over time.
The conditions in each reaction were identical,
except that each reaction was carried out using
a different catalyst.

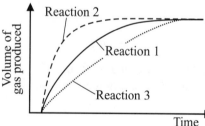

Which reaction was carried out using the most effective catalyst?
Give a reason for your answer.

....

....

[2]

15

Mixed Tests for Paper 1

Test 24

⏱ 10

There are **11 questions** in this test. Give yourself **10 minutes** to answer them all.

1. The reaction of chlorine with butane is a...

   A   ...substitution reaction.

   B   ...addition reaction.

   C   ...neutralisation reaction.

   [1]

2. Which of these metal ions forms a blue precipitate in a reaction with sodium hydroxide solution?

   A Fe^{3+}

   B Cu^{2+}

   C Fe^{2+}

   [1]

3. Which of the following best describes the structure of diamond?

   A   Layers of carbon atoms arranged in hexagons

   B   Rigid giant covalent structure

   C   Giant ionic lattice

   [1]

4. Which of the following **cannot** be used to show that a sample of a solid, soluble dye is impure?

   A   Melting point data

   B   Paper chromatography

   C   Distillation

   [1]

5. Which of the following reactions is reversible?

   A   Dehydration of copper(II) sulfate

   B   Combustion of methane

   C   Displacement of iodine from sodium iodide solution by chlorine

   [1]

6. Which of the following statements about crude oil is correct?

   A   All the compounds in crude oil have the same boiling point.

   B   Crude oil is a mixture of hydrocarbons.

   C   The components of crude oil can be separated using filtration.

   [1]

7. Which of the following metals is the most reactive?

   A   Aluminium

   B   Magnesium

   C   Sodium

   [1]

8. A reaction which takes in energy from the surroundings is described as...

   A   ...an endothermic reaction.

   B   ...a reduction reaction.

   C   ...an exothermic reaction.

   [1]

9. Give **one** example of a catalyst that is used in the catalytic cracking of hydrocarbons.

    ....
    [1]

10. Name the four most abundant gases present in dry air.
    Give the approximate percentage abundance of each gas.

    Gas: ....   Abundance: ....

    Gas: ....   Abundance: ....

    Gas: ....   Abundance: ....

    Gas: ....   Abundance: ....
    [4]

11. Copper has two stable isotopes, copper-63 and copper-65.
    Copper-63 has an abundance of 69.2%.
    Copper-65 has an abundance of 30.8%.

    Calculate the relative atomic mass of copper.

    ....

    ....

    ....

    ....

    Relative atomic mass = ...
    [2]

    15

Test 25

⏱ 10

There are **11 questions** in this test. Give yourself **10 minutes** to answer them all.

1. True or False? "A displayed formula shows all of the bonds between the atoms in a compound."

   A True

   B False

   [1]

2. Which of the following would react with copper oxide to produce copper sulfate?

   A Hydrochloric acid

   B Sulfuric acid

   C Nitric acid

   [1]

3. What is the formula of an ammonium ion?

   A NH_3^+

   B NH_4^+

   C NO_3^-

   [1]

4. What is the electronic configuration of neon?

   A 2.2.6

   B 2.8.8

   C 2.8

   [1]

5. When magnesium burns in air...

   A ...a bright white flame will be seen.

   B ...water is produced.

   C ...the product of the reaction will contain hydrogen.

   [1]

6. How many moles of water will be present in 3 moles of $CuSO_4.5H_2O$?

   A 3 moles

   B 5 moles

   C 15 moles

   [1]

7. How many carbon-carbon single bonds are there in a molecule of ethene?

   A 0

   B 1

   C 2

   [1]

8. Which of the following reactions will produce a gas that turns limewater milky?

   A Sodium hydroxide + hydrochloric acid

   B Magnesium carbonate + sulfuric acid

   C Lithium + sulfuric acid

   [1]

9. The theoretical yield of product X from a reaction is 81 g. The actual yield is 59 g.
    Calculate the percentage yield of product X.

    ....

    ....

    Percentage yield = ... %

    [2]

10. A student carried out a series of tests on an unknown compound.
    Here are the results of the tests:

    1) Adding sodium hydroxide to a solution of the compound produced a green precipitate.

    2) Adding dilute nitric acid and then silver nitrate to a solution of the compound
       produced a cream precipitate.

    Identify the metal ion and the non-metal ion present in the compound.

    Metal ion: ....

    Non-metal ion: ....

    [2]

11. Using collision theory, explain how breaking a solid reactant up into smaller pieces will
    affect the rate of a reaction.

    ....

    ....

    ....

    ....

    ....

    [3]

    $$\boxed{ \atop 15}$$

Test 26

There are **11 questions** in this test. Give yourself **10 minutes** to answer them all.

1. True or False? "Non-metals are found on the left-hand side of the Periodic Table."

   A   True

   B   False

   [1]

2. Kerosene is commonly used as a...

   A   ...fuel for large ships.

   B   ...fuel for cars.

   C   ...fuel for aircraft.

   [1]

3. What colour flame do Ca^{2+} ions produce in a flame test?

   A   Blue-green

   B   Orange-red

   C   Yellow

   [1]

4. Which of the following could **not** be used to prevent iron from rusting?

   A   Oxidising the iron

   B   Oiling the iron

   C   Galvanising the iron

   [1]

5. The reaction of hydrogen peroxide to form water and oxygen is...

   A   ...a neutralisation reaction.

   B   ...a combustion reaction.

   C   ...a decomposition reaction.

   [1]

6. Which of the following compounds would **not** form a solution if added to water?

   A   Calcium chloride

   B   Calcium sulfate

   C   Calcium nitrate

   [1]

7. True or False? "The molar enthalpy change for a combustion reaction can be calculated by dividing the heat energy change by the number of moles of fuel burned."

   A   True

   B   False

   [1]

8. Which of the following is a pair of organic compounds which both contain 4 hydrogen atoms?

   A   Methane and ethene

   B   Butane and butene

   C   Ethane and butene

   [1]

9. An element has the electronic configuration 2.8.4.

Which group of the periodic table must it be in? Explain your answer.

....

....

[2]

10. A 53.8 g sample of copper chloride contains 25.4 g of copper and 28.4 g of chlorine.
Determine the empirical formula of copper chloride.

Relative atomic masses (A_r): Cl = 35.5, Cu = 63.5

....

....

....

....

....

[3]

11. A student adds some bromine water to a sample of propene. A reaction occurs.
Draw the displayed formula of the organic compound formed in this reaction.
Name the compound you have drawn.

....

[2]

15

Mixed Tests for Paper 2

Test 27

There are **11 questions** in this test. Give yourself **10 minutes** to answer them all.

1. Which of the following explains why solid metals can conduct electricity?

    A They have a giant structure.

    B They are held together by strong electrostatic attraction.

    C They contain delocalised electrons.

    [1]

2. In electrolysis, at the negatively charged electrode, cations...

    A ...are oxidised.

    B ...are reduced.

    C ...dissolve.

    [1]

3. The reactivity of Group 1 elements increases as you go down the group, because...

    A ...it becomes easier for the atom to attract an extra electron.

    B ...it becomes easier for the atom to lose an outer electron.

    [1]

4. Decreasing the pressure of a gaseous reversible reaction at equilibrium will cause the equilibrium position to...

    A ...move in the direction where there are fewer molecules of gas.

    B ...move in the endothermic direction.

    C ...move in the direction where there are more molecules of gas.

    [1]

5. True or False? "Esters can be used as food flavourings."

    A True

    B False

    [1]

6. True or False? "Glucose can ferment to produce ethanol in the absence of air."

    A True

    B False

    [1]

7. Which process can be used to find the amount of acid required to neutralise a given quantity of alkali?

    A Distillation

    B Titration

    C Electrolysis

    [1]

8. In an endothermic reaction, the energy released when bonds are formed is...

    A ...less than the energy used in breaking old bonds.

    B ...greater than the energy used in breaking old bonds.

    [1]

9. A molecule of an organic compound is shown on the right.

Name the compound, and state **one** way in which it could be converted to a carboxylic acid.

....

....

[2]

10. Zinc metal is less reactive than carbon.

What process could be used to extract zinc from its ore?
Explain your answer.

....

....

....

[2]

11. The equation for the formation of ammonia is: $N_2 + 3H_2 \rightarrow 2NH_3$
The enthalpy change of this reaction is -97 kJ mol^{-1}.
Draw and label a reaction profile for this reaction on the axes below.
Label the enthalpy change of the reaction.

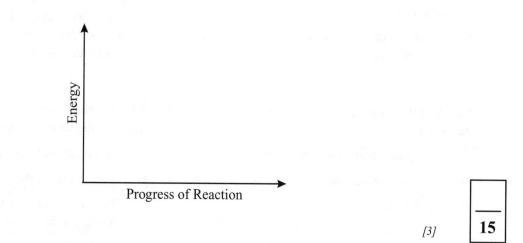

[3]

15

PAPER 2

There are **11 questions** in this test. Give yourself **10 minutes** to answer them all.

1. Why is fermentation **not** carried out at temperatures higher than 30 °C in industry?

   A   The enzyme in the yeast denatures at these temperatures.

   B   The fermentation reaction is faster at these temperatures.

   [1]

2. True or False? "Pure metals can be bent because the layers of atoms can slide over each other."

   A   True

   B   False

   [1]

3. A gaseous reversible reaction has reached a dynamic equilibrium. Which of the following would **not** affect the equilibrium position of the reaction?

   A   Changing the temperature

   B   Changing the pressure

   C   Using a catalyst

   [1]

4. A particular ester has the structural formula $CH_3CH_2COOCH_3$. This ester can be formed from...

   A   ...methanol and propanoic acid.

   B   ...ethanol and ethanoic acid.

   C   ...butanol and methanoic acid.

   [1]

5. Solubility is a measure of the maximum mass of...

   A   ...solute that can dissolve in a set mass of solvent.

   B   ...solution that can dissolve in a set mass of solvent.

   C   ...solvent that can dissolve in a set mass of solute.

   [1]

6. Simple molecular substances cannot conduct electricity, because...

   A   ...the intermolecular forces are too strong.

   B   ...they don't have any charged particles that are able to move.

   C   ...they have an equal number of positively-charged and negatively-charged particles.

   [1]

7. Stainless steel is used to make cutlery, because it...

   A   ...is a good conductor of heat.

   B   ...is corrosion-resistant.

   C   ...is flexible.

   [1]

8. Which of the following would you need to calculate the enthalpy change of a reaction?

   A   The energies of the reactant bonds only.

   B   The energies of the product bonds only.

   C   The energies of both the reactant and the product bonds.

   [1]

9. Molten lead(II) bromide ($PbBr_2$) is electrolysed using inert electrodes.
Write a balanced half equation for the reaction that occurs at the anode.

....

[1]

10. When calcium chloride solution is added to magnesium sulfate solution,
a precipitate of calcium sulfate is formed.
Describe the next steps required to obtain a pure, dry sample of calcium sulfate.

....

....

....

....

....

[3]

11. What mass, in g, of carbon dioxide is formed when 120 dm³ of oxygen
reacts with methane at room temperature and pressure (RTP)?
The relative formula mass of CO_2 is 44. The molar volume of a gas at RTP is 24 dm³.

$$CH_{4\,(g)} + 2O_{2\,(g)} \rightarrow CO_{2\,(g)} + 2H_2O_{(g)}$$

....

....

....

....

....

.... g

[3]

15

Test 29

There are **11 questions** in this test. Give yourself **10 minutes** to answer them all.

1. Ethanoic acid reacts with magnesium to form a magnesium ethanoate salt and one other product. What is this other product?

   A Hydrogen

   B Carbon dioxide

   C Water

   [1]

2. Metallic bonding is the electrostatic attraction between positively charged metal ions and negatively charged...

   A ...metal ions.

   B ...pairs of shared electrons.

   C ...delocalised electrons.

   [1]

3. An ionic compound will **not** conduct electricity if it is...

   A ...in an aqueous solution.

   B ...molten.

   C ...a solid.

   [1]

4. True or False? "All metals are found in the Earth's crust as metal ores."

   A True

   B False

   [1]

5. Which of the following is **not** a method used to extract metals from their ores?

   A Reduction of ores by carbon

   B Oxidation of ores by carbon

   C Electrolysis

   [1]

6. An increase in temperature shifts the position of a dynamic equilibrium...

   A ...in the direction of the endothermic reaction.

   B ...in the direction of the exothermic reaction.

   [1]

7. How are polyesters formed?

   A Addition polymerisation

   B Condensation polymerisation

   C Cracking

   [1]

8. What is an alloy?

   A A giant covalent substance made up of metal and oxygen atoms.

   B A metal extracted from its ore using electrolysis.

   C A mixture of a metal and one or more elements.

   [1]

9. Name the **two** substances formed in the electrolysis of a sodium chloride solution using inert electrodes. Explain your reasoning for each one.

1. ....

....

2. ....

....

[4]

10. Give the name of the compound shown below.

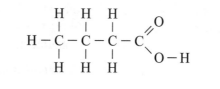

....

[1]

11. A certain reaction is carried out with and without a catalyst.
Which line on the graph shows the reaction with a catalyst? Explain your answer.

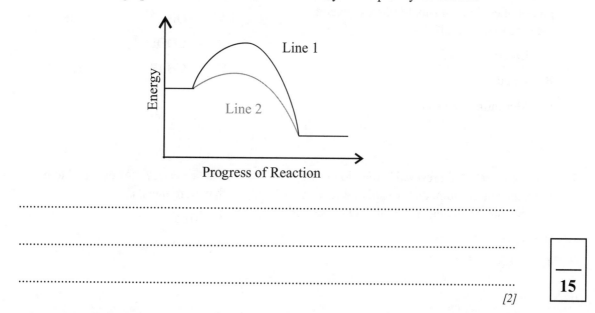

....

....

....

[2]

15

Test 30

There are **10 questions** in this test. Give yourself **10 minutes** to answer them all.

1. True or False? "A reversible reaction occurring in a sealed container can reach a dynamic equilibrium."

   A   True

   B   False

   [1]

2. What type of compound is ethyl ethanoate?

   A   A carboxylic acid

   B   An ester

   C   An alkene

   [1]

3. True or False? "Metals that are above aluminium in the reactivity series can be extracted from their ores by reduction using carbon."

   A   True

   B   False

   [1]

4. Ethanol can be manufactured by reacting ethene with steam under certain conditions. Which of the following is **not** used to manufacture ethanol in this way?

   A   Temperature of 300 °C

   B   Pressure of 60-70 atmospheres

   C   Iron catalyst

   [1]

5. An acid is slowly added to an alkali in a titration experiment. Which of the following pieces of equipment should you use to add the acid to the alkali?

   A   Burette

   B   Pipette

   C   Measuring cylinder

   [1]

6. Which of the following is the functional group of a carboxylic acid?

   A   —OH

   B   —COOH

   C   —CH$_2$Cl

   [1]

7. True or False? "If a reversible reaction is at dynamic equilibrium, its forward and reverse reaction are occurring at the same rate."

   A   True

   B   False

   [1]

8. True or False? "Alloys tend to be softer than pure metals."

   A   True

   B   False

   [1]

---

9. A 25.0 cm³ sample of potassium hydroxide (KOH) solution
   has a concentration of 0.200 mol dm⁻³.
   This sample is completely neutralised by 40.0 cm³ of sulfuric acid (H_2SO_4).

$$2KOH + H_2SO_4 \rightarrow K_2SO_4 + 2H_2O$$

Find the concentration of the sulfuric acid in mol dm⁻³.

....

....

....

....

....

....

.... mol dm⁻³

[4]

10. The Haber process produces ammonia (NH_3) using the following chemical reaction:

$$N_{2\,(g)} + 3H_{2\,(g)} \rightleftharpoons 2NH_{3\,(g)}$$

The Haber process is carried out under a high pressure.
Explain why this improves the yield of ammonia and the rate of the reaction.

....

....

....

....

....

....

[3]

15

Answers

Section 1 — Particles and Mixtures

Test 1 — Pages 2–3

1. C *[1 mark]* 2. B *[1 mark]*
3. A *[1 mark]* 4. C *[1 mark]*
5. B *[1 mark]* 6. A *[1 mark]*
7. C *[1 mark]* 8. B *[1 mark]*
9. Isotopes are different atoms/atomic forms of the same element, which have the same number of protons but different numbers of neutrons *[1 mark]*.
10. The solution would appear less red *[1 mark]*, as the food colouring particles would become more spread out/the solution would be diluted *[1 mark]*.
11. The student should place a spot of the ink on a starting line, marked in pencil, near the bottom of a strip of filter paper *[1 mark]*. They should place the bottom of the filter paper in a beaker containing a small amount of solvent *[1 mark]* so the ink is above the solvent level *[1 mark]*.
12. E.g. the ice/water is impure *[1 mark]*.

Test 2 — Pages 4–5

1. B *[1 mark]* 2. A *[1 mark]*
3. B *[1 mark]* 4. C *[1 mark]*
5. A *[1 mark]* 6. B *[1 mark]*
7. C *[1 mark]* 8. A *[1 mark]*
9. $R_f = 3.2 \div 4.9$
   $= 0.6530...$ *[1 mark]*
   $= 0.65$ (to 2 s.f.) *[1 mark]*
10. A pure substance will always leave a single spot on the chromatography paper *[1 mark]*. An impure substance will usually leave multiple spots *[1 mark]*.
11. The solubility of compound X increases as the temperature increases *[1 mark]*.
   From the graph, the solubility of compound X at 70 °C is 22 g per 100 g of solvent *[1 mark]*. So the maximum mass of compound X that could dissolve in 200 g of solvent at 70 °C is $2 \times 22 = 44$ g *[1 mark]*.

Section 2 — The Periodic Table and Bonding

Test 3 — Pages 6–7

1. C *[1 mark]* 2. A *[1 mark]*
3. C *[1 mark]* 4. A *[1 mark]*
5. A *[1 mark]* 6. B *[1 mark]*
7. C *[1 mark]* 8. B *[1 mark]*
9. They have the same number of outer electrons/electrons in their outer shell *[1 mark]*.
10. Group 0 *[1 mark]*
   The noble gases don't easily lose or gain electrons *[1 mark]*.
11. Sodium chloride is made up of positive (sodium) ions and negative (chloride) ions in a regular arrangement *[1 mark]*. The oppositely charged ions in sodium chloride are strongly attracted to one another by electrostatic forces *[1 mark]*.
12. The solution would have a pH of e.g. 4 (accept any value less than 7) *[1 mark]*. This is because boron oxide is a non-metal oxide, and non-metal oxides are (usually) acidic *[1 mark]*.

Test 4 — Pages 8–9

1. A *[1 mark]* 2. B *[1 mark]*
3. B *[1 mark]* 4. B *[1 mark]*
5. A *[1 mark]* 6. A *[1 mark]*
7. B *[1 mark]* 8. C *[1 mark]*
9. The two oxygen atoms share two pairs of electrons *[1 mark]*. This forms a double covalent bond *[1 mark]*.
10. Lithium, sodium and potassium are all in the same group/Group 1 *[1 mark]*, so they all have the same number of electrons/one electron in their outer shell *[1 mark]*.
11. X = metal/potassium ions
   Y = delocalised/free electrons
   [1 mark]
   The delocalised/free electrons in potassium are able to move through the structure and conduct electricity *[1 mark]*. The layers of the metal ions in potassium can slide over each other, so it is malleable *[1 mark]*.

Section 3 — Equations, Calculations and Electrolysis

Test 5 — Pages 10–11

1. B *[1 mark]* 2. A *[1 mark]*
3. C *[1 mark]* 4. A *[1 mark]*
5. C *[1 mark]* 6. B *[1 mark]*
7. A *[1 mark]* 8. A *[1 mark]*
9. $2Li + 2H_2O \rightarrow 2LiOH + H_2$ *[1 mark for values shown, or any multiple or fraction of these values that gives a correctly balanced equation]*
10. 0.00025 kg $\times 1000 = 0.25$ g *[1 mark]*
   moles = mass $\div M_r$
   $= 0.25 \div (23 + 16 + 1)$
   $= 0.00625$ moles *[1 mark]*
   concentration = moles $\div$ volume
   $= 0.00625 \div 0.5$
   $= 0.0125$ mol dm^{-3} *[1 mark]*
   [Or 3 marks for the correct answer via any other method.]
11. Strongly heat the magnesium in the crucible with the lid on, but with a gap to allow oxygen in. Stop heating when the magnesium has turned completely white *[1 mark]*. Reweigh the crucible, lid and its contents (once they have cooled), and subtract the known masses to determine the mass of oxygen used in the reaction *[1 mark]*. Convert the masses of magnesium and oxygen to mol, and use the relative amounts in mol to determine the empirical formula *[1 mark]*.

Test 6 — Pages 12–13

1. C *[1 mark]* 2. A *[1 mark]*
3. A *[1 mark]* 4. B *[1 mark]*
5. B *[1 mark]* 6. C *[1 mark]*
7. C *[1 mark]* 8. A *[1 mark]*
9. $Pb^{2+} + 2e^- \rightarrow Pb$ *[1 mark]*
10. Number of moles of C = mass $\div A_r$
   $= 66$ g $\div 12 = 5.5$
   From balanced equation, 1 mole of C reacts to produce 1 mole of CO_2, so 5.5 moles of C produces 5.5 moles of CO_2 *[1 mark]*.
   Relative formula mass (M_r) of CO_2
   $= 12 + (2 \times 16) = 44$ *[1 mark]*.

Answers

Mass of CO_2 = moles × M_r
= 5.5 × 44 = 242 g *[1 mark]*
[Or 3 marks for the correct answer via any other method.]

11. mass of Fe = 10.5 g
mass of O = 14.5 − 10.5 = 4.0 g
moles of Fe = mass ÷ A_r
= 10.5 ÷ 56 = 0.1875 moles
moles of O = mass ÷ A_r
= 4.0 ÷ 16 = 0.25 moles *[1 mark]*
Divide by the smallest number of moles (0.1875):
Fe = 0.1875 ÷ 0.1875 = 1
O = 0.25 ÷ 0.1875 = $\frac{4}{3}$
So for every 1 atom of Fe, there are $\frac{4}{3}$ atoms of O *[1 mark]*.
Multiply by 3 to get whole numbers:
Fe = 3, O = 4
So the empirical formula of the iron oxide is Fe_3O_4 *[1 mark]*.
[Or 3 marks for the correct answer via any other method.]

Section 4 — Inorganic Chemistry

Test 7 — Pages 14–15
1. B *[1 mark]*   2. C *[1 mark]*
3. C *[1 mark]*   4. A *[1 mark]*
5. B *[1 mark]*   6. A *[1 mark]*
7. C *[1 mark]*   8. A *[1 mark]*
9. Bubble the gas through the limewater. If the gas is carbon dioxide, the limewater will turn cloudy/milky *[1 mark]*.
10. The solution will change from red to yellow *[1 mark]*.
11. E.g. silver chloride *[1 mark]*, lead(II) chloride *[1 mark]*
12. The reaction of magnesium with hydrochloric acid would produce a lot of bubbles/effervescence *[1 mark]*. The reaction of iron with hydrochloric acid would be less vigorous/produce fewer bubbles than with magnesium *[1 mark]*. Magnesium reacts faster than iron because magnesium is more reactive/higher in the reactivity series than iron *[1 mark]*.

Test 8 — Pages 16–17
1. A *[1 mark]*   2. C *[1 mark]*
3. B *[1 mark]*   4. B *[1 mark]*
5. C *[1 mark]*   6. A *[1 mark]*
7. C *[1 mark]*   8. B *[1 mark]*
9. Hold the loop in a Bunsen burner flame until the loop burns without any colour *[1 mark]*. Dip the loop into the sample, and place it in the clear blue part of the Bunsen burner flame, and observe the colour of the flame produced *[1 mark]*.
10. Carbon dioxide in the Earth's atmosphere absorbs the heat that is radiated from the Earth *[1 mark]* and re-radiates the heat in all directions (including back towards the Earth) *[1 mark]*. If the amount of carbon dioxide in the atmosphere increases, a greater amount of heat will be re-radiated back towards the Earth, and the temperature of the Earth's surface will increase *[1 mark]*.
11. As you move down the group, the outer electron is further away from the nucleus *[1 mark]*. So it is less strongly attracted to the nucleus and is lost more easily *[1 mark]*.

Test 9 — Pages 18–19
1. A *[1 mark]*   2. B *[1 mark]*
3. C *[1 mark]*   4. B *[1 mark]*
5. A *[1 mark]*   6. A *[1 mark]*
7. B *[1 mark]*   8. C *[1 mark]*
9. Gently heat the solution using a Bunsen burner to evaporate off some of the water *[1 mark]*. Leave the solution to cool and allow the salt to crystallise *[1 mark]*. Filter off the solid salt and leave it to dry *[1 mark]*.
10. A white precipitate will form *[1 mark]*.
11. The halogens decrease in reactivity down the group *[1 mark]*. This is because atomic radius increases down the group/the outer shell of electrons is further from the nucleus *[1 mark]*, so it is harder to attract/gain an extra electron *[1 mark]*.

Test 10 — Pages 20–21
1. B *[1 mark]*   2. A *[1 mark]*

3. A *[1 mark]*   4. B *[1 mark]*
5. C *[1 mark]*   6. A *[1 mark]*
7. C *[1 mark]*   8. B *[1 mark]*
9. Potassium is above copper in the reactivity series *[1 mark]*, as potassium reacts with water but copper does not *[1 mark]*.
10. E.g. gold *[1 mark]*, as it is unreactive/inert/very low in the reactivity series *[1 mark]*.
11. Percentage of oxygen in the air =
$\frac{\text{Start volume - Final volume}}{\text{Start volume}} \times 100$
$= \frac{59.0 - 47.0}{59.0} \times 100$ *[1 mark]*
$= \frac{12.0}{59.0} \times 100 = 20.338...\%$ *[1 mark]*
= 20.3% (to 3 s.f.)
[1 mark]
[Or 3 marks for the correct answer via any other method.]

Test 11 — Pages 22–23
1. A *[1 mark]*   2. A *[1 mark]*
3. C *[1 mark]*   4. A *[1 mark]*
5. C *[1 mark]*   6. B *[1 mark]*
7. B *[1 mark]*   8. A *[1 mark]*
9. Place a damp piece of red litmus paper in the gas *[1 mark]*. The litmus paper will turn blue if ammonia is present/the solution contains ammonium ions *[1 mark]*.
10. Proton acceptor: Na_2CO_3 *[1 mark]* Proton donor: H_2SO_4 *[1 mark]*
11. $Pb(NO_3)_{2(aq)} + MgSO_{4(aq)} \rightarrow PbSO_{4(s)} + Mg(NO_3)_{2(aq)}$ *[1 mark]* Deionised water contains no dissolved ions *[1 mark]*. If normal water was used/deionised was not used, then the salt would be contaminated with some of the ions that were dissolved in the water *[1 mark]*.

Test 12 — Pages 24–25
1. A *[1 mark]*   2. B *[1 mark]*
3. B *[1 mark]*   4. A *[1 mark]*
5. C *[1 mark]*   6. B *[1 mark]*
7. C *[1 mark]*   8. B *[1 mark]*
9. In barrier methods, the iron is coated with a barrier material (e.g. paint/grease) *[1 mark]*. This prevents water and oxygen from coming into contact with the iron, and so prevents

the iron from rusting *[1 mark]*.
10. $H^+ + OH^- \rightarrow H_2O$ *[1 mark]*
    7 *[1 mark]*
11. E.g. sodium is more reactive/higher in the reactivity series than titanium *[1 mark]*, so can displace titanium from $TiCl_4$ *[1 mark]*. Titanium could not be extracted in this way using zinc/iron/copper/silver/gold *[1 mark]*.

Section 5 — Physical Chemistry

Test 13 — Pages 26–27

1. C *[1 mark]*   2. A *[1 mark]*
3. B *[1 mark]*   4. C *[1 mark]*
5. B *[1 mark]*   6. C *[1 mark]*
7. C *[1 mark]*   8. B *[1 mark]*
9. Increasing the concentration of a solution increases the number of reactant particles in a given volume/ causes the particles to move closer together *[1 mark]*. This will increase the frequency of collisions/cause the particles to collide more often *[1 mark]*.
10. Change in temperature, $\Delta T = 53$ °C
    Heat energy transferred to water
    $= m \times c \times \Delta T$
    $= 150 \times 4.2 \times 53$
    $= 33\,390$ J $= 33.39$ kJ *[1 mark]*
    Moles of methanol that reacted
    $= $ mass $\div M_r = 1.64 \div 32$
    $= 0.05125$ moles *[1 mark]*
    Molar enthalpy change
    $= $ heat transferred to water $\div$ moles of methanol used
    $= -33.39 \div 0.05125$
    $= -651.512...$ kJ/mol
    $= -650$ kJ/mol (to 2 s.f.) *[1 mark]*
    [Or 3 marks for correct answer via any other method]
11. The equilibrium would move towards the right *[1 mark]*, because the right hand side of the equation contains fewer molecules of gas *[1 mark]*.

Test 14 — Pages 28–29

1. B *[1 mark]*   2. C *[1 mark]*
3. B *[1 mark]*   4. C *[1 mark]*
5. A *[1 mark]*   6. A *[1 mark]*
7. C *[1 mark]*   8. A *[1 mark]*

9. E.g. experiment 2 could have been carried out at a higher temperature / with a greater concentration of reactants / at a higher pressure (with gases) / with a catalyst / with solid reactants crushed into smaller parts *[1 mark]*. This would have increased the rate of reaction, as shown by the steeper gradient of the line *[1 mark]*.
10. The reaction has a negative enthalpy change (because it is exothermic) *[1 mark]*.
11. Energy required to break the bonds in the reactants:
    $4(C–H) + 2(O=O)$
    $= (4 \times 413) + (2 \times 496)$
    $= 2644$ kJ/mol *[1 mark]*
    Energy released when forming new bonds in the products:
    $2(C=O) + 4(O–H)$
    $= (2 \times 803) + (4 \times 464)$
    $= 3462$ kJ/mol *[1 mark]*
    So the enthalpy change/ΔH
    $= 2644 - 3462$ *[1 mark]*
    $= -818$ kJ/mol *[1 mark]*
    [Or 4 marks for the correct answer via any other method.]

Test 15 — Pages 30–31

1. B *[1 mark]*   2. B *[1 mark]*
3. B *[1 mark]*   4. A *[1 mark]*
5. C *[1 mark]*   6. B *[1 mark]*
7. B *[1 mark]*   8. A *[1 mark]*
9. E.g. carry out the reaction in a conical flask attached to a gas syringe *[1 mark]*. Record the volume of carbon dioxide gas produced at regular time intervals until the reaction has finished *[1 mark]*. Repeat the experiment using a different concentration of hydrochloric acid whilst keeping all other variables the same *[1 mark]*.
    [Or 3 marks for another valid experimental method, such as measuring the loss of mass as the carbon dioxide gas is produced.]
10. It shows an exothermic reaction. The products are at a lower energy than the reactants *[1 mark]*, so energy is released and the reaction must be exothermic *[1 mark]*.

11. E.g. the student could cool the mixture of ammonia and hydrogen chloride gases produced *[1 mark]*. A white solid should form, showing the reaction is reversible *[1 mark]*.

Section 6 — Organic Chemistry

Test 16 — Pages 32–33

1. B *[1 mark]*   2. A *[1 mark]*
3. C *[1 mark]*   4. B *[1 mark]*
5. C *[1 mark]*   6. B *[1 mark]*
7. B *[1 mark]*   8. A *[1 mark]*
9. E.g. they can make more bonds. / They contain fewer hydrogen atoms than the alkane with the same number of carbon atoms. / They contain at least one carbon-carbon double bond *[1 mark]*.
10. There is a temperature gradient in the column/the column gets cooler as you go up it *[1 mark]*. The fractions have different boiling points *[1 mark]* so they condense and drain out at different levels *[1 mark]*.
11. Poly(propene) is an addition polymer *[1 mark]*.
    E.g. addition polymers are not biodegradable/are inert so do not break down easily in the environment *[1 mark]*. Burning addition polymers can release toxic gases into the environment *[1 mark]*.

Test 17 — Pages 34–35

1. A *[1 mark]*   2. B *[1 mark]*
3. C *[1 mark]*   4. B *[1 mark]*
5. C *[1 mark]*   6. A *[1 mark]*
7. B *[1 mark]*   8. A *[1 mark]*
9. E.g. sulfur dioxide *[1 mark]*, oxides of nitrogen *[1 mark]*
10.

pentane *[1 mark]*
11. Vaporised hydrocarbons are passed over a silica/alumina catalyst *[1 mark]* at temperatures of $600 - 700$ °C *[1 mark]*. When the hydrocarbons come into contact with the catalyst, they are broken down

Answers

into alkenes and short-chain alkanes *[1 mark]*.

Test 18 — Pages 36–37

1. A *[1 mark]*   2. B *[1 mark]*
3. A *[1 mark]*   4. C *[1 mark]*
5. B *[1 mark]*   6. C *[1 mark]*
7. A *[1 mark]*   8. B *[1 mark]*
9. Poly(ethene)/polythene *[1 mark]*. Ethene molecules have C=C double bonds which can open up and join together to form a chain *[1 mark]*.
10. $Br_2 + C_3H_6 \rightarrow C_3H_6Br_2$ *[1 mark]*
11. The sulfuric acid is a catalyst for the reaction *[1 mark]*. Ethyl ethanoate *[1 mark]* (and) water *[1 mark]*.

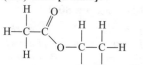
[1 mark]

Test 19 — Pages 38–39

1. C *[1 mark]*   2. A *[1 mark]*
3. B *[1 mark]*   4. C *[1 mark]*
5. A *[1 mark]*   6. C *[1 mark]*
7. C *[1 mark]*   8. A *[1 mark]*
9.
$$H{-}C{=}C{-}F \text{ (with H, F substituents)}$$
[1 mark]
10. The solution will change from orange to colourless *[1 mark]*. The C=C bond in the alkene opens up/is split, and a bromine atom is added to each of the carbon atoms in the double bond *[1 mark]*, forming a dibromoalkane *[1 mark]*.
11. but-2-ene *[1 mark]*
E.g.
$$C{=}C{-}C{-}C$$
[1 mark]

$$C{=}C \text{ structure}$$
[1 mark]

Test 20 — Pages 40–41

1. A *[1 mark]*   2. B *[1 mark]*

3. A *[1 mark]*   4. C *[1 mark]*
5. A *[1 mark]*   6. B *[1 mark]*
7. C *[1 mark]*   8. B *[1 mark]*
9. $I_2 + C_4H_{10} \rightarrow C_4H_9I + HI$ *[1 mark]* Two possible isomers could be produced *[1 mark]*.
10. carbon monoxide *[1 mark]* carbon/soot *[1 mark]*
11. (Catalytic) cracking is used to convert the hydrocarbons in bitumen into the hydrocarbons in kerosene *[1 mark]*. There is a greater demand for short-chain hydrocarbons than for long-chain hydrocarbons *[1 mark]*, but the supply of long-chain hydrocarbons from crude oil fractions is greater than that of short-chain hydrocarbons *[1 mark]*.

Test 21 — Pages 42–43

1. A *[1 mark]*   2. B *[1 mark]*
3. B *[1 mark]*   4. C *[1 mark]*
5. A *[1 mark]*   6. B *[1 mark]*
7. C *[1 mark]*   8. C *[1 mark]*
9. A phosphoric acid/H_3PO_4 catalyst is used *[1 mark]*. The reaction is carried out at a temperature of 300 °C *[1 mark]* and a pressure of 60-70 atm *[1 mark]*.
10.

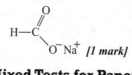
[1 mark]

$$H{-}O{-}C{-}C{-}O{-}H$$
[1 mark]

11. $2HCOOH + 2Na \rightarrow 2HCOONa + H_2$ *[1 mark]*

$$H{-}C(=O){-}O^- Na^+$$ *[1 mark]*

Mixed Tests for Paper 1

Test 22 — Pages 44–45

1. B *[1 mark]*   2. A *[1 mark]*
3. B *[1 mark]*   4. A *[1 mark]*
5. A *[1 mark]*   6. C *[1 mark]*

7. B *[1 mark]*   8. C *[1 mark]*
9. E.g. to make sure all the acid has reacted. / To make sure there is no leftover acid in the product *[1 mark]*.
10. alkanes *[1 mark]*
E.g. a hydrogen atom from the alkane is replaced with a bromine atom *[1 mark]*. This is a substitution reaction *[1 mark]*.
11. Mass of mixture = 25 + 25 = 50 g *[1 mark]*
$Q = m \times c \times \Delta T$
   $= 50 \times 4.2 \times 18.5$ *[1 mark]*
   $= 3885$ J
   $= 3.885$ kJ *[1 mark]*
[Or 3 marks for the correct answer via any other method.]

Test 23 — Pages 46–47

1. C *[1 mark]*   2. B *[1 mark]*
3. A *[1 mark]*   4. C *[1 mark]*
5. B *[1 mark]*   6. A *[1 mark]*
7. C *[1 mark]*   8. B *[1 mark]*
9. Name: butane *[1 mark]*
Empirical formula: C_2H_5 *[1 mark]*
10. E.g. add water to the mixture to dissolve the soluble magnesium sulfate *[1 mark]*. Filter the mixture to remove the insoluble copper filings *[1 mark]*. Crystallise the remaining solution to obtain a pure sample of the magnesium sulfate *[1 mark]*.
11. Reaction 2 *[1 mark]*, as reaction 2 formed the product at the fastest rate/in the shortest time *[1 mark]*.

Test 24 — Pages 48–49

1. A *[1 mark]*   2. B *[1 mark]*
3. B *[1 mark]*   4. C *[1 mark]*
5. A *[1 mark]*   6. B *[1 mark]*
7. C *[1 mark]*   8. A *[1 mark]*
9. E.g. silica/alumina *[1 mark]*
10. Nitrogen, 78% *[1 mark]*
Oxygen, 21% *[1 mark]*
Argon, 1% *[1 mark]*
Carbon dioxide, 0.04% *[1 mark]*
11. Relative atomic mass = [sum of (relative isotopic mass × isotopic abundance)] ÷ (sum of abundances)
$= \dfrac{((63 \times 69.2) + (65 \times 30.8))}{(69.2 + 30.8)}$
[1 mark]

Answers

= 63.616

= 63.6 (to 3 s.f.) *[1 mark]*

[Or 2 marks for the correct answer via any other method.]

Test 25 — Pages 50–51

1. A *[1 mark]*   2. B *[1 mark]*
3. B *[1 mark]*   4. C *[1 mark]*
5. A *[1 mark]*   6. C *[1 mark]*
7. A *[1 mark]*   8. B *[1 mark]*
9. Percentage yield = (actual yield ÷ theoretical yield) ×100
   = (59 ÷ 81) × 100 *[1 mark]*
   = 72.8...% = 73% (to 2 s.f.) *[1 mark]*
   [Or 2 marks for the correct answer via any other method.]
10. Iron(II) / Fe^{2+} *[1 mark]*
    Bromide / Br^- *[1 mark]*
11. It will increase the rate of the reaction *[1 mark]* because the surface area to volume ratio of the solid is increased *[1 mark]*, meaning collisions can occur more frequently between reactants *[1 mark]*.

Test 26 — Pages 52–53

1. B *[1 mark]*   2. C *[1 mark]*
3. B *[1 mark]*   4. A *[1 mark]*
5. C *[1 mark]*   6. B *[1 mark]*
7. A *[1 mark]*   8. A *[1 mark]*
9. Group 4 *[1 mark]*, as it has four electrons in its outer shell *[1 mark]*.
10. Moles = mass ÷ M_r
    moles (copper) = 25.4 ÷ 63.5 = 0.4
    moles (chlorine) = 28.4 ÷ 35.5 = 0.8
    [1 mark]
    Ratio of Cu : Cl = 0.4 : 0.8
    = 1 : 2 *[1 mark]*
    So empirical formula = $CuCl_2$
    [1 mark]
11. E.g.

    H Br Br
    | | |
    H—C—C—C—H
    | | |
    H H H   *[1 mark]*

    dibromopropane *[1 mark]*

Mixed Tests for Paper 2

Test 27 — Pages 54–55

1. C *[1 mark]*   2. B *[1 mark]*
3. B *[1 mark]*   4. C *[1 mark]*
5. A *[1 mark]*   6. A *[1 mark]*

7. B *[1 mark]*   8. A *[1 mark]*
9. Ethanol *[1 mark]*
   E.g. heat with potassium dichromate (VI) in dilute sulfuric acid / microbial oxidation in air *[1 mark]*.
10. The zinc ore could be reduced with carbon *[1 mark]*, because carbon is more reactive than zinc, so it displaces the zinc from its ore and allows the zinc metal to be extracted *[1 mark]*.
11.

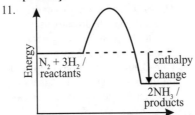

Progress of Reaction

[1 mark for labelled product line below and to the right of labelled reactant line, 1 mark for correct shape of curve linking reactants to products, 1 mark for correct labelling of enthalpy change]

Test 28 — Pages 56–57

1. A *[1 mark]*   2. A *[1 mark]*
3. C *[1 mark]*   4. A *[1 mark]*
5. A *[1 mark]*   6. B *[1 mark]*
7. B *[1 mark]*   8. C *[1 mark]*
9. $2\,Br^- \rightarrow Br_2 + 2\,e^-$ *[1 mark]*
10. E.g. filter out the precipitate from the solution using filter paper and a filter funnel *[1 mark]*. Rinse the precipitate and filter paper with deionised water *[1 mark]*. Leave the calcium sulfate to dry in an oven/ desiccator *[1 mark]*.
11. Volume (dm^3) = moles of gas × 24
    Moles of O_2 = 120 ÷ 24
    = 5 moles *[1 mark]*
    From the balanced equation, 2 moles of O_2 react to produce 1 mole of CO_2, so 5 moles of O_2 react to produce 2.5 moles of CO_2 *[1 mark]*.
    Mass of CO_2 = moles × M_r
    = 2.5 × 44 = 110 g *[1 mark]*.
    [Or 3 marks for the correct answer via any other method.]

Test 29 — Pages 58–59

1. A *[1 mark]*   2. C *[1 mark]*
3. C *[1 mark]*   4. B *[1 mark]*
5. B *[1 mark]*   6. A *[1 mark]*
7. B *[1 mark]*   8. C *[1 mark]*
9. Hydrogen gas *[1 mark]*, because e.g. sodium is more reactive than hydrogen *[1 mark]*. Chlorine gas *[1 mark]*, because e.g. chloride ions are present in the solution *[1 mark]*.
10. butanoic acid *[1 mark]*
11. Line 2, because it has a lower initial rise in energy than line 1 *[1 mark]*, which shows the activation energy has been lowered by a catalyst *[1 mark]*.

Test 30 — Pages 60–61

1. A *[1 mark]*   2. B *[1 mark]*
3. B *[1 mark]*   4. C *[1 mark]*
5. A *[1 mark]*   6. B *[1 mark]*
7. A *[1 mark]*   8. B *[1 mark]*
9. Convert 25.0 cm^3 and 40.0 cm^3 to dm^3:
   Volume of KOH = 25.0 ÷ 1000
   = 0.0250 dm^3
   Volume of H_2SO_4 = 40.0 ÷ 1000
   = 0.0400 dm^3 *[1 mark]*
   Number of moles of KOH
   = concentration × volume
   = 0.200 × 0.0250
   = 0.00500 mol *[1 mark]*
   From the equation, 2 moles of KOH react with 1 mole of H_2SO_4, so there were 0.00500 ÷ 2 = 0.00250 moles of H_2SO_4 in the acid solution *[1 mark]*.
   So acid concentration = moles ÷ volume = 0.00250 ÷ 0.0400
   = 0.0625 mol dm^{-3} *[1 mark]*
   [Or 4 marks for the correct answer via any other method.]
10. There are fewer molecules of gas products than gas reactants *[1 mark]*. This means increasing the pressure favours the forward reaction, resulting in a higher yield of ammonia *[1 mark]*. Increased pressure also increases the rate of reaction, because there are more gas particles in a given volume, so the frequency of collisions between particles will increase *[1 mark]*.